KIDS' ADVENTURES

WITH

E.T. FRIENDS IN SPACE

BASED ON REAL ACCOUNTS

STORIES OF FRIENDSHIP AND LEARNING
BETWEEN HUMAN KIDS AND EXTRATERRESTRIALS

BARBARA LAMB, AUTHOR • MARY EDWARDS, ILLUSTRATOR

LEDGE MEDIA

DEAR READER,

WHEN WE BECAME MOMS, WE LEARNED THE VALUE OF READING TOGETHER WITH OUR CHILDREN AND ENCOURAGED THEM TO KEEP AN OPEN MIND. WE DEDICATE THIS BOOK TO ALL CHILDREN, AND GRANDCHILDREN, WHO ARE THE PIONEERS OF THE FUTURE. WE HOPE TO INSPIRE YOUNG MINDS TO THE MAGIC OF THE UNIVERSE AND TO OTHER POSSIBILITIES OF "OTHER-WORLDLY" SURPRISES! IT'S UP TO FUTURE SPACE EXPLORERS TO DISCOVER NEW INFORMATION ABOUT THE UNIVERSE. ENJOY!

Barbara Lamb & Mary Edwards

Special Thanks to my rocket-scientist father, Bob Edwards, for navigating me to the Stars as a child, and for inspiring me to create this book to support other children's belief that E.T.s are here to teach and support us and to my children, Lizzy and Alex Roberts -- Mary

ENJOY OUR NEW EDITION!

**The world and everyone changed during Covid and so did we!
We have republished this book in hopes it reaches and inspires even more
children and families. This is the first book *ever* for children about *real* kids
experiences with extraterrestrial beings.**

A LITTLE BACKGROUND...

Millions of people worldwide are recognizing that they have been visited by and taken away by other-worldly beings. These beings have gradually been identified as 'extraterrestrial' beings who seem to be coming from other planets in unusual spacecrafts. Interest in this phenomenon has been increasing since the early 1980s, with many people's sightings of UFOs and orbs, and expressed in many UFO conferences, ongoing UFO organizations, films, interviews, blogs, televisions specials, YouTube specials, and books. The scenarios in this book are taken from 6,000 hypnotic regression sessions conducted by Barbara Lamb with people who either knew or suspected they had experienced encounters with these unusual beings. These scenarios are accurately illustrated by Mary Edwards, who first experienced contact with ETs on a craft at age 3. She was not validated by her parents or anyone so spent decades thinking she was crazy. This book is her lifelong dream to prepare children to navigate their fears. A typical reaction to having these unfamiliar beings nearby is fear: fear of their differentness and fear of the unknown..."who/what are they and what do they want with me?" Mary knows now that the ET have been guiding, teaching and supporting her since childhood and now understands the positive importance of their contacts.

There are many different species of extraterrestrial beings, ranging from more scary looking ones to friendly, benevolent, loving beings. These visitations and abductions usually begin during a person's childhood, although they might not be remembered until later in life. Children (and adults) have a variety of reactions to seeing unusual nonhuman beings nearby. Some are startled by their appearance, some are curious about them, some feel fear, and some welcome them as playmates and friends. Regressions with children and with adults often surprisingly show the beings as caring and helpful to them, including healing them of a variety of serious health problems and teaching them wonderful skills. Often procedures which seem to be unwanted and unacceptable turn out to be beneficial to those experiencing them.

Hopefully reading this book to children will assist parents in helping their children who have encountered these beings, and may possibly be helping themselves. We wish to open their awareness of other intelligent lives in the universe and of the benefits of knowing each other. Many of them are very interested in us humans, and we can learn to reciprocate with interest in them and learn a lot from them.

"I'M ALWAYS EXCITED WHEN MY SPACE FRIENDS LET ME SEE EARTH THROUGH THE BIG WINDOW. REALLY COOL! NONE OF THE OTHER KIDS AT HOME GET TO SEE THIS."

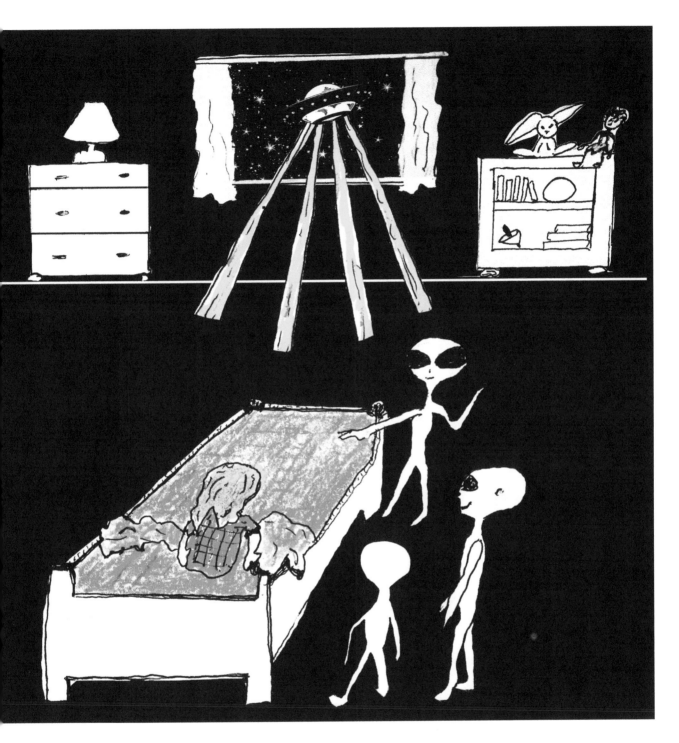

"SOMETIMES I WAKE UP IN THE MIDDLE OF THE NIGHT, AND MY SPACE
FRIENDS AND LOTS OF BRIGHT LIGHT COME IN THROUGH THE WINDOW.
I USED TO BE SCARED OF THEM, BUT NOW I'M HAPPY TO SEE THEM. THEY
FLOAT ME UP AND THROUGH THE WALL. WE FLY UP THROUGH THE AIR
AND INTO THEIR SPACESHIP FOR LOTS OF ADVENTURES."

"I LOVE BEING PULLED UP IN A BIG BEAM OF LIGHT! IT FEELS LIKE I'M FLYING!
THIS HAPPENS AT NIGHT AND SOMETIMES IN THE DAYTIME TOO."

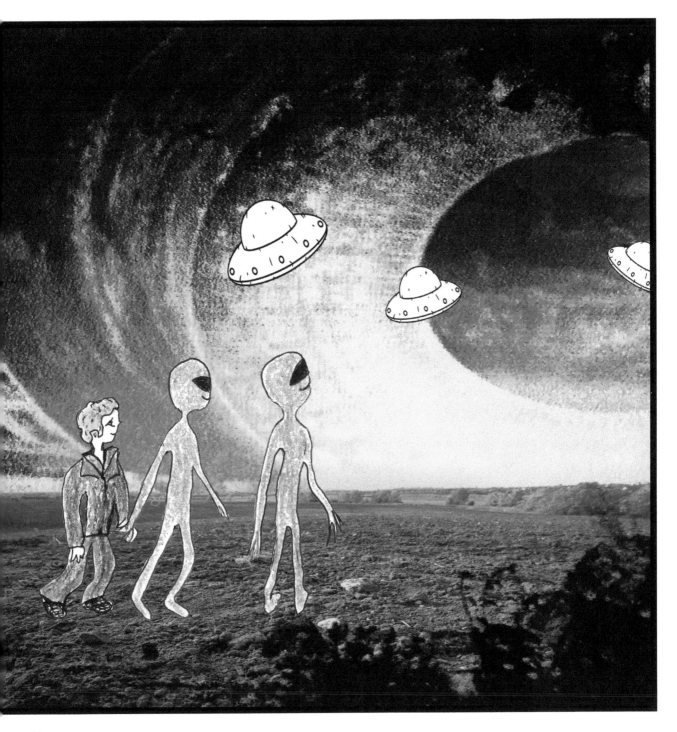

"SOMETIMES MY SPACE FRIENDS TAKE ME TO A BIG OPENING IN THE SKY.
THEY SAY IT'S A PORTAL. I WONDER WHAT'S OUT THERE?
I GET TO HAVE ALL THESE ADVENTURES!"

"SOMETIMES WHEN I CAMP OUT IN MY BACKYARD THEY COME AND TAKE ME ON THEIR SPACESHIP. OH GOODIE! I GET TO SEE MY SPACE FRIENDS!"

"It's exciting that they're teaching me to fly their spacecraft. They tell me when I grow up I'll fly their ship once in awhile!"

"SOMETIMES WHEN I'M SICK MY SPACE FRIENDS PUT ME IN A BIG TUB OF GREEN GOO. IT'S WEIRD, BUT IT MAKES ME FEEL BETTER.

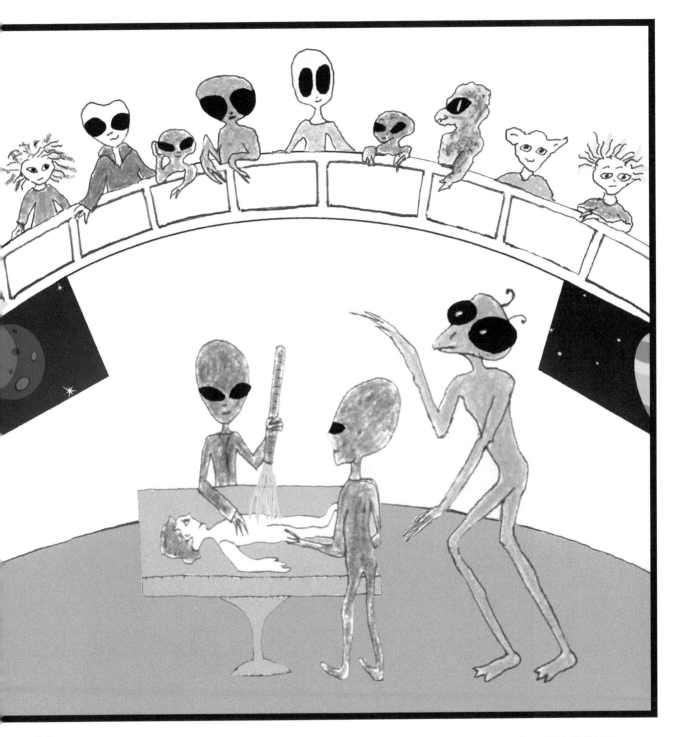

"ON THE SHIP MY SPACE FRIENDS POKE AROUND AND CHECK MY BODY.
IF THERE IS SOMETHING WRONG INSIDE, THEY HEAL ME WITH LIGHT.
OTHERS WATCH ME FROM A GALLERY ABOVE US."

"I LOVE IT WHEN THIS BEAUTIFUL BLUE LADY TEACHES ME TO HEAL WITH ENERGY FROM MY HANDS. I THINK OF HER AS AN ANGEL, SHE SAYS SHE'S AN ARCTURIAN."

"SOMETIMES ONE OF MY SPACE FRIENDS STARES INTO MY EYES AND GIVES ME LOTS OF INFORMATION. SOMETIMES HE SEEMS TO SEE AND KNOW ABSOLUTELY EVERYTHING ABOUT ME."

"THEY ARE SO KIND! THEY GIVE ME DARK LIQUID TO DRINK WHEN I'M TIRED OR DON'T FEEL WELL. THEY REALLY CARE ABOUT ME."

"ONE OF THE MOST FUN THINGS ON THE SPACESHIP IS BEING TAUGHT TO MOVE THINGS ONLY WITH OUR MINDS. MY SPACE FRIENDS AND HYBRID KIDS AND OTHER EARTH FRIENDS ARE ABLE TO DO THIS. WE STARTED BY MOVING A SMALL FEATHER, THEN A SMALL PAPER, THEN A PING PONG BALL, AND NOW A BEACHBALL. WE HAVE TO STARE AT THE BALL AND THINK OF PUSHING IT ONLY WITH OUR MINDS AND NOT WITH OUR HANDS OR FEET. WE PUSH IT ACROSS THE CIRCLE AND BACK AGAIN."

"SOMETIMES I WAKE UP IN THE MIDDLE OF THE NIGHT AND HAVE THE
STRONGEST URGE TO GET ON MY BIKE AND RIDE INTO THE WOODS.
I GO TO A SECRET SCHOOL THERE WITH OTHER KIDS, AND MY
SPACE FRIEND TEACHES US SPECIAL SKILLS.
MY EARTH TEACHERS DON'T DO THAT."

ON THE SPACESHIP, THEY SOMETIMES TAKE ME TO A CLASSROOM WHERE THEY
TEACH ME MANY THINGS. THEY SHOW ME A "MOVIE" OF REALLY BAD THINGS
HAPPENING ON OUR EARTH: HURRICANES, FLOODS, VOLCANOES ERUPTING,
ARTHQUAKES, TIDAL WAVES, TORNADOES, FIRES, AND BOMBS EXPLODING. THEY
AY I SHOULD TELL PEOPLE TO BE PREPARED. THEY REALLY CARE ABOUT US AND
EARTH. THEY ARE AMAZED AT ALL THE ANIMALS AND LIFE FORMS WE HAVE ON
EARTH. NO OTHER PLANET HAS SO MANY DIFFERENT KINDS OF LIFE."

"I CAN SEE THROUGH THESE VERY LOVING BEINGS. THEY SWAY LIKE SEAWEED IN THE OCEAN. THEY TELL ME TO LET PEOPLE KNOW ABOUT THEM AND MY OTHER SPACE FRIENDS. THEY SAY IT'S TIME TO LET PEOPLE KNOW ON EARTH THERE ARE MANY OTHERS IN SPACE, AND MANY ARE VERY GOOD."

"I HAVE FUN PLAYING WITH MY SPACE FRIENDS IN THE HALLWAY OF THE
SPACESHIP. THEY LOOK AND ACT A LITTLE DIFFERENTLY THAN MY FRIENDS AT
HOME, BECAUSE THEY ARE HYBRIDS. THAT MEANS THEY ARE PART ET-SPACE
FRIENDS AND PART HUMAN LIKE ME. I SEE GROWN UP HYBRIDS TOO.
THEY NEVER SMILE, BUT THEY ARE NICE."

"MY COUSIN LIVES IN ZIMBABWE, AFRICA. ONE DAY DURING RECESS, A BIG
SILVER SHIP LANDED NEAR THE SCHOOL PLAY YARD. A LITTLE GRAY MAN
WITH REALLY BLACK EYES TOLD HER TO TELL EVERYONE TO TAKE GOOD
CARE OF OUR EARTH. HE SAID OUR EARTH IS IN TROUBLE AND
NEEDS EVERYONE'S HELP."

THEY TELL ME THAT WHEN I GROW UP I CAN GO TO THE GALACTIC FEDERATION COUNCIL MEETINGS WITH MANY DIFFERENT KINDS OF SPACE FRIENDS FROM MANY PLANETS. I CAN BE ONE OF THE PEOPLE WHO SPEAK FOR PLANET EARTH."

REVIEWS

"ET friends in Space, what a delightful and charming book. I loved the beautifully illustrated artwork, as well as the information which explains the reality of Extraterrestrial encounters in pictures. Acknowledging the reality children do have these off world experiences, but in delightf[ul] non-threatening format. I believe it will be an important aid when parents discover this is relevar[t] to their child. It can help both parents and their children to understand what these experiences can mean. I have six grandchildren and would not hesitate to give them this charming book, which not only educates the new awake generations, but helps to normalize experiences which are far more prevalent globally than the public realize. A real gift and highly recommended. "
--Mary Rodwell Principal of ACERN, author Awakening and The New Human

"What a lovely book! It will link readers in deep communion with our ancient heritage and will embolden their walk on the path to the stars."
--William Henry, author Cloak of the Illuminati: Secrets, Transformations, Crossing the Stargate, Oracle of the Illuminati: Contact, Co-Creation, Coincidence, Mary Magdalene: the Illuminator: The Woman Who Enlightened Christ, The Peacemaker and the Key of Life

"Barbara Lamb and Mary Edwards have created a beautiful and important book. Kids' Adventures with E.T.Friends in Space makes a vital contribution to children and the families of children whose experiences have included close encounters. These experiences can be frightening, disorienting, and isolating, but also wonder-making and life-changing. Families are often unsure how to enable conversations about their children's experiences, and how to help their children to open up and share experiences they may not understand. This book enables children to acknowledge their own unusual experiences and include their families in a way that will provide them with the reassurance of acceptance, love and understanding. Together, Barbara and Mary have created a disarmingly simple book, which I believe will bring help and inspiration to countless families who are encountering the challenge of nurturing such conversations with their children. I know of no other book on the market that does this at all – let alone so gently and compassionately. I am full of admiration for Barbara and Mary's courage in helping us break the taboos of our culture surrounding close encounters and ET contact, and in taking care of the needs and vulnerabilities of children and families who are often distressed and disoriented by such experiences. I have no doubt this beautiful book will soon become a much loved companion for many."
-- Paul Wallis, author Escaping from Eden and The Scars of Eden

Printed in the USA
CPSIA information can be obtained
at www.ICGtesting.com
LVHW070734261023
761976LV00013B/291